Diez Deditos
TEN LITTLE FINGERS
&
Other Play Rhymes and Action Songs from Latin America

Selected, Arranged, and Translated by
JOSÉ-LUIS OROZCO

Illustrated by
ELISA KLEVEN

SCHOLASTIC INC.
New York Toronto London Auckland Sydney
Mexico City New Delhi Hong Kong

P9-CCO-533

Para mi papá, Fernando,
Para mi mamá, Susana,
Para mi abuelita, María Victoria,
y para todos los niños del mundo.
¡Viva la música!

Special thanks to "el maestro" Roberto Chiófalo,
Gary Soto, and Carolyn Soto
J.-L.O.

To Julie, Anne, Mavis, Marissa, Stacey, Susie, and Ashley,
with thanks for friendship and inspiration
E.K.

No part of this publication may be reproduced in whole or in part,
or stored in a retrieval system, or transmitted in any form or by any means,
electronic, mechanical, photocopying, recording, or otherwise,
without written permission of the publisher. For information regarding permission,
write to Dutton Children's Books, a division of Penguin Books USA Inc.,
375 Hudson Street, New York, NY 10014.

ISBN 0-439-14982-7

All lyrics and music arrangements copyright © 1997 by José-Luis Orozco.
Illustrations copyright © 1997 by Elisa Kleven.
Black-and-white diagrams copyright © 1997 by Judy Lanfredi. All rights reserved.
Published by Scholastic Inc., 555 Broadway, New York, NY 10012, by arrangement with
Dutton Children's Books, a division of Penguin Books USA Inc. SCHOLASTIC and
associated logos are trademarks and/or registered trademarks of Scholastic Inc.

12 11 10 9 8 7 6 5 4 3 2 1   9/9 0 1 2 3 4/0

Printed in the U.S.A.   08

First Scholastic printing, November 1999

Designed by Sara Reynolds

All of the songs contained in this book have been recorded
by José-Luis Orozco and are available on CD and cassette tape
from Arcoiris Records, P.O. Box 7428, Berkeley, CA 94707.

Preface

Centuries of children's traditions from Spanish-speaking countries are represented in this bilingual collection of finger rhymes and action songs. Many of them I learned from my mother and grandmother in Mexico City, and others from the families I lived with while traveling in Latin America and Spain as a singer with the Mexico City Children's Choir. Still other songs and rhymes are my own creations. Over the past twenty-seven years I have had a wonderful time teaching and performing them—for preschoolers, elementary-school children, teachers, parents, even newborns! I hope every soul may have fun year-round singing, clapping, dancing—and enjoying the many themes included here, such as animals, musical instruments, parts of the body, language sounds, and, of course, family and self-esteem.

¡Ay, ay, ay!	*Ay, ay, ay!*
¡Ahora es cuando chile verde¡	*It's now or never, chili pepper!*
¡Hay que darle sabor al caldo!	*Let's spice up the soup!*
Con cantos y tradiciones	*With heaps of songs old and new*
que les traigo de a montones,	*That I bring to you,*
¡Levanto mi voz al viento	*My voice rises with the wind*
para alegrar corazones¡	*To cheer your hopeful hearts.*
¡Yo soy José-Luis Orozco!	*I am José-Luis Orozco!*
¡Para servirles a ustedes!	*To guide you on this tour!*
¡Yyyyy nooos vaaaamos!	*So, my friends, o-o-off we-e-e go-o-o!!!!!*

J.-L.O.

Contents

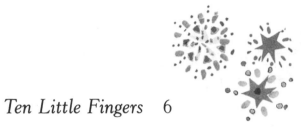

Diez deditos · Ten Little Fingers

Sway your open hands while singing the first three lines and then close them on the fourth. Then hold up your fingers one after another, starting with the pinkie of one hand, then the ring finger, the tall man, and so on, following the numbers in the verses.

Dos ma - ni - tas, diez de - di - tos, dos ma - ni - tas, diez de - di - tos,

dos ma - ni - tas, diez de - di - tos, cuén - ta - los con - mi - go.

Dos manitas, diez deditos,
dos manitas, diez deditos,
dos manitas, diez deditos,
cuéntalos conmigo.

Two little hands, ten little fingers,
two little hands, ten little fingers,
two little hands, ten little fingers,
count them all with me.

Uno, dos, tres deditos,

One, two, three little fingers,

cuatro, cinco, seis deditos,

four, five, six little fingers,

siete, ocho, nueve deditos,

seven, eight, nine little fingers,

y uno más son diez.

and one more makes ten.

Tengo manita · I Have a Little Hand

This was my favorite rhyme when I was small. Before or after la merienda (evening supper) at my abuelita's (grandmother's) house—which included chocolate drinks and pan dulce (Mexican pastry)—all the grandchildren would wait in line for a chance to sit on our grandmother's lap and have her act out this play rhyme with us. It still reminds me of those special times with her. Take the child's arm and move it gently up and down so that the child's loosely hanging hand moves up and down, too. Older children can shake their arms for themselves.

Tengo manita,
no tengo manita,
porque la tengo
desconchabadita.

[*repetir la rima*]

I have a little hand,
I don't have a little hand,
because my little hand
is out of hand.

[*repeat the rhyme*]

San Severino • San Severino

This song, also called "San Sereni" or "San Sereni de la Buena Vida," is popular in the Spanish-speaking communities of the world. The version here comes from Puerto Rico. Clap your hands as you sing the first two lines of the song, then imitate the profession or trade mentioned in the song. Make the motions of the laundress scrubbing clothes; the tortilla maker making tortillas (since that's a clapping motion, clap here, too); the carpenter sawing wood; the secretary typing; the teacher working with children by writing on the chalkboard or saying good morning. Many other jobs/skills/trades could be added.

San Se-ve-ri-no de la bue-na, bue-na vi-da,

San Se-ve-ri-no de la bue-na, bue-na vi-da. A-

sí, a-sí, a-sí, ha-cía la la-van-de-ra, a-

sí, a-sí, a-sí, a-sí me gus-ta a mí.

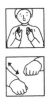
San Severino de la buena, buena vida,
San Severino de la buena, buena vida.

Así, así, así,
hacía **la lavandera,**
así, así, así,
así me gusta a mí.

San Severino of the happy, happy life,
San Severino of the happy, happy life.
The laundress washes the clothes.
She likes to work all day.
She likes to work all day.
I like to do it, too.

Repeat, replacing the words in boldface with the following words and phrases:

la tortillera

The tortilla maker (clap, clap, clap)

(Lyrics continued on next page)

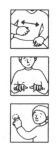 el carpintero

The carpenter makes tables.

la secretaria

The secretary types letters.

la maestra

The teacher works with children.

¡Sí se puede! · Yes, I Can!

I dedicate this poem to all the children of the world, in love, honor, and friendship. Start with your hands above your head to show the world. Then tap your chest with both thumbs three times. Keep one hand on your chest and tap your forehead to show "intelligent." Then raise one arm above your head to show "reaching your goals." Lower it slightly, making a relaxed fist. Bring both palms to your chest, make a strong fist, and hold it to show "Yes, I can!"

En este mundo
tan lindo y tan grande
yo soy único,
yo soy especial,
lleno de amor
y de inteligencia.

*In this beautiful
and great world
I am unique,
I am very special,
and full of love.
I am intelligent.*

Yo puedo realizar
mis sueños
siendo un buen estudiante
y haciendo siempre mi trabajo
con amor,
con orgullo
y con gusto,
porque sé que
¡sí se puede!

*I can reach
my goals
by being a good student
and by always doing my work
with love,
with pride,
and with pleasure.*

Yes, I can!

Vamos a cantar · Let's Sing

This is a song I wrote while working for several school districts in the San Francisco Bay area in the early seventies. It's a very good song for group participation. For each verse, perform or pretend to perform the action that is listed—from singing through snoring—and end with clapping.

A ho - ra va-mos a can - tar, a can - tar, a can - tar. A ho - ra

va - mos a can - tar, a can - tar, a can - tar.

 Ahora vamos **a cantar**,
a cantar, a cantar.

[*cantar dos veces*]

*Everybody **sing** now,*
sing *now,* **sing** *now.*

[*sing twice*]

Repeat the song, each time replacing the words in boldface with one of the words below.

	a leer	*read*
	a escribir	*write*
	a comer	*eat*
	a silbar	*whistle*
	a reír	*laugh*
	a bailar	*dance*
	a saltar	*jump*
	a roncar	*snore*
	a aplaudir	*clap*

Sun, sun, ba, ba, e · Sun, Sun, ba, ba, e

I first heard this song about a beautiful bird as a small boy in Mexico, and then from a family in Pôrto Alegre, Brazil, during my childhood journeys with the Mexico City Children's Choir. Later I heard it again in Cuba. Tap the rhythm of the first two lines on your thighs. For the second two, use your hands as beaks to suggest a bird singing at dawn. Then move your hands in a zigzag for the second verse; pretend you are flying; use your hands as beaks again; jump; and pretend to go to sleep. You can also sing the verses as call-and-response, with the responders repeating the words that the caller sings.

Sun, sun, sun, sun, sun ba, ba, e. Pá-ja-ro lin-do de la ma-dru-gá. Pá-ja-ro lin-do, sun, sun.

Canto y respuestaj 1°: solista, 2°: todos
Call and Response 1°: solo, 2°: all

Sun, sun, sun, sun, sun, ba, ba, e. Sun, sun, sun, sun, sun, ba, ba, e.	*Sun, sun, sun, sun, sun, ba, ba, e.* *Sun, sun, sun, sun, sun, ba, ba, e.*
Pájaro lindo de la madrugá. Pájaro lindo de la madrugá.	*Beautiful bird in the dawn of day.* *Beautiful bird in the dawn of day.*
Pájaro lindo, sun, sun. Pájaro lindo, sun, sun.	*Beautiful bird, sun, sun.* *Beautiful bird, sun, sun.*
Vuela, vuela, sun, sun. Vuela, vuela, sun, sun.	*Fly, fly, sun, sun.* *Fly, fly, sun, sun.*
Canta, canta, sun, sun. Canta, canta, sun, sun.	*Sing, sing, sun, sun.* *Sing, sing, sun, sun.*
Salta, salta, sun, sun. Salta, salta, sun, sun.	*Jump, jump, sun, sun.* *Jump, jump, sun, sun.*
Duerme, duerme, sun, sun. Duerme, duerme, sun, sun.	*Go to sleep, sun, sun.* *Go to sleep, sun, sun.*
[cantar dos veces]	[sing twice]

Debajo del botón · Under a Button

In this rhyme about a mouse found under a button, an adult taps his or her index finger gently on the child's chest (or button, if there is one) each time the words ton, ton or tin, tin are sung. Older children can tap for themselves. For variation, clap the hands on ton, ton or tin, tin, or tap without singing. For even more variety, clap on every syllable of the song. After a few times, you may want to leave out some words and clap them instead.

De - ba - jo del bo - tón, tón, tón,   que en - con - tró Mar - tín, tín, tín,

ha - bí - a un ra - tón, tón, tón.   Ay,   qué chi - qui - tín, tín, tín.

Ay,   qué chi - qui - tín, tín, tín,   e - ra el ra - tón, tón, tón,

que en - con - tró Mar - tín, tín, tín, de - ba - jo del bo - tón, tón, tón.   De -

[*repetir*]

Debajo del botón, tón, tón,
que encontró Martín, tín, tín,
había un ratón, tón, tón.
Ay, qué chiquitín, tín, tín.

Ay, qué chiquitín, tín, tín,
era el ratón, tón, tón,
que encontró Martín, tín, tín,
debajo del botón, tón, tón.

*Under a button, ton, ton, ton,
found by Uncle Martin, tin,
there was mouse Patón, ton, ton,
playing tin, tin, tin, tin, tin.*

*Playing tin, tin, tin, tin, tin,
there was mouse Patón, ton, ton,
found by Uncle Martin, tin,
under a button, ton, ton, ton.*

Una rata vieja · Pancha, the Old Rat

This is an old, old song, just like the old, old rat in the song. Sing this and act it out. Make a wrinkled face to show the old rat; pretend you are ironing; pretend that you burned your tail (make an "ouch!" face); apply ointment to your hand; wrap a cloth around it; and then show what is left of the poor rat's tail by bringing your thumb and index finger close together.

U - na ra - ta vie - ja, que e - ra plan - cha - do - ra,

por plan - char su fal - da ¡se que - mó la co - la!

 Una rata vieja,

Pancha, the old rat,

 que era planchadora,
por planchar su falda

was ironing one day,
and when she pressed her skirt,

 ¡se quemó la cola!

she burned her tail away!

Se puso pomada.

She applied some ointment.

Se amarró un trapito.

She wrapped it in a veil,

 Y a la pobre rata
le quedó un rabito.

but the poor old Pancha,
she lost most of her tail.

Pimpón · Pimpón

I learned this song from my grandmother Doña María Victoria Ramos de Orozco, who learned it in Jalisco, Mexico. Children in Spanish-speaking countries know it very well. In a circle, sing the words and act them out. Hold up your hands to show Pimpón's hands. Pretend you are washing your face, your hands, combing your hair, wiping away tears, and shaking hands. Open and close your fingers to show the twinkling stars. Make a pillow of your hands, "Good night."

Pim - pón es un mu - ñe - co con ma - nos de car - tón. Se la - va la ca - ri - ta con a - gua y con ja - bón.

Pimpón es un muñeco
con manos de cartón.
Se lava la carita
con agua y con jabón.

Pimpón is a nice puppet
with hands made out of paper.
He likes to wash his face
with soap and lots of water.

Pimpón es un muñeco
con manos de cartón.
Se lava las manitas
con agua y con jabón.

Pimpón is a nice puppet
with hands made out of paper.
He likes to wash his hands
with soap and lots of water.

Se desenreda el pelo
con peine de marfil.
Y aunque no le gusta,
no llora, ni hace así.

Pimpón fixes his hair
with a comb or with a brush.
Although he doesn't like it,
he doesn't make a fuss.

Pimpón, dame la mano
con un fuerte apretón,
que quiero ser tu amigo—
Pimpón, Pimpón, Pimpón.

Pimpón shakes hands with me
with a big, happy smile.
He likes to be my friend—
Pimpón, Pimpón, Pimpón.

Y cuando las estrellas
comienzan a salir,
Pimpón se va a la cama,
Pimpón se va a dormir.

And when the stars are blinking
up in the pretty sky,
Pimpón closes his eyes,
and he whispers, "Good night."

Juanito · Little Johnny

In this delightful song, you get to shake, jiggle, and twist different parts of your body as you sing. Clap your hands. Then in the first verse, wiggle your pinkie back and forth; in the second, shake your foot and then wiggle your pinkie. In the third verse, bend your knee up and down, then shake your foot and wiggle your pinkie. Every time you sing a new verse, add a movement until you've got your whole body in motion, from head to toe!

Jua - ni - to cuan-do bai - la, bai - la, bai - la, bai - la. Jua -

ni - to cuan-do bai - la, bai - la con el de - di - to, con el de -

di - to, i - to, i - to A - sí bai - la Jua - ni - to.

* *repetir como quiera / repeat as needed*

Juanito cuando baila,
baila, baila, baila.
Juanito cuando baila,
baila con el dedito,
con el dedito, ito, ito.

Así baila Juanito.

When little Johnny dances,
he dances, dances, dances.
When little Johnny dances,
he dances with his pinkie,
with his pinkie, pinkie, pinkie.

That's how little Johnny dances.

Juanito cuando baila,
baila, baila, baila.
Juanito cuando baila,
baila con el pie,
con el pie, pie, pie,

con el dedito, ito, ito.

Así baila Juanito.

When little Johnny dances,
he dances, dances, dances.
When little Johnny dances,
he dances with his foot,
with his foot, foot, foot,

with his pinkie, pinkie, pinkie.

That's how little Johnny dances.

Juanito cuando baila…   *When little Johnny dances…*

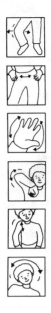 la rodilla, dilla, dilla…   *knee…*

la cadera, dera, dera…   *hip…*

la mano, mano, mano…   *hand…*

el codo, codo, codo…   *elbow…*

el hombro, hombro, hombro…   *shoulder…*

la cabeza, eza, eza…   *head…*

19

La Pulga • The Flea Market
de San José · of San Jose

The colorful flea market of San Jose, California, reminds me of many beautiful marketplaces in Latin America. In 1971, I recorded this joyful traditional song, which I had learned as "La feria de Atitlán," on a childhood trip through Guatemala. In Puerto Rico and Mexico, the song is also known as "La feria de San Juan." Clap on the chorus, then pretend you are playing the guitar, clarinet, violin, cello, and drum. As you imitate in Spanish the sounds of the musical instruments, you will be making the sounds of the five Spanish vowels.

En la Pul - ga de San Jo - sé yo com - pré u - na gui - ta - rra, ta - rra ta - rra ta - rra, la gui - ta - rra. Va - ya us - ted, va - ya us - ted a la Pul - ga de San Jo - sé. Va - ya us - ted, va - ya us - ted a la Pul - ga de San Jo - sé.

* *repetir con los demás instrumentos / repeat this section with the other instruments*

En la Pulga de San José
yo compré una guitarra,
tarra, tarra, tarra, la guitarra.

CORO
Vaya usted, vaya usted
a la Pulga de San José.

[cantar dos veces]

In the Flea Market of San Jose
I bought a guitar,
tarra, tarra, tarra, the guitar.

CHORUS
You can go, you can go
to the Flea Market of San Jose.

[sing twice]

(Lyrics continued on next page)

En la Pulga de San José
yo compré un clarinete,
nete, nete, nete, el clarinete,
tarra, tarra, tarra, la guitarra.

Vaya usted…

En la Pulga de San José
yo compré un violín,
lín, lín, el violín,
nete, nete, nete, el clarinete,
tarra, tarra, tarra, la guitarra.

Vaya usted…

En la Pulga de San José
yo compré un violón,
lón, lón, el violón,
lín, lín, el violín,
nete, nete, nete, el clarinete,
tarra, tarra, tarra, la guitarra.

Vaya usted…

En la Pulga de San José
yo compré un tumtum,
tum, tum, el tumtum,
lón, lón, el violón,
lín, lín, el violín,
nete, nete, nete, el clarinete,
tarra, tarra, tarra, la guitarra.

In the Flea Market of San Jose
I bought a clarinet,
net, net, net, the clarinet,
tarra, tarra, tarra, the guitar.

You can go…

In the Flea Market of San Jose
I bought a violin,
lin, lin, the violin,
net, net, net, the clarinet,
tarra, tarra, tarra, the guitar.

You can go…

In the Flea Market of San Jose
I bought a cello,
low, low, the cello,
lin, lin, the violin,
net, net, net, the clarinet,
tarra, tarra, tarra, the guitar.

You can go…

In the Flea Market of San Jose
I bought a drum,
tum, tum, the tum-tum,
low, low, the cello,
lin, lin, the violin,
net, net, net, the clarinet,
tarra, tarra, tarra, the guitar.

Mi familia · My Family

This little verse for the fingers is well known all over Latin America. Children can point to their own fingers, starting with the thumb and ending with the baby finger, or an adult can touch each finger of the child's hand in turn.

Este chiquito es mi hermanito.	*This tiny one is my little brother.*
Esta es mi mamá.	*This one is my mother.*
Este altito es mi papá.	*This tall one is my father.*
Esta es mi hermana.	*This one is my sister.*
Y éste(a) chiquito(a) y bonito(a) soy yo.	*And this little and pretty one is me.*

Este chiquito y bonito · This One Is Little and Pretty

This starts with the baby finger and moves over to the thumb. The verse can be recited to a small child, touching his or her fingers in turn. Or kids can say it themselves and point to their fingers.

Este chiquito y bonito.	*This one is little and pretty.*
Este, señor de anillitos.	*This one is Mr. Ring Man.*
Este, tonto loco.	*This one is Mr. Tall Man.*
Este se va a la escuela/lame cazuelas.	*This one goes to school/licks the pots.*
Y éste se lo come todo.	*And this one eats everything.*

Cuando vayas · When You Go to
al mercado   the Marketplace

This is a favorite tickling rhyme of children. The child sits on the lap of an adult or older brother or sister who recites the rhyme. The adult moves a hand in a chopping motion up the child's body, first chopping right above the knee, then the thigh, the chest or upper arm, and arriving at the shoulder. At the end of the song, the adult tickles the child's ribs or neck. Older children can act out the hand motions themselves.

Cuando vayas al mercado,
no compres carne de aquí,

When you go to the marketplace,
don't buy meat from here

ni de aquí,

nor here

ni de aquí,

nor here

ni de aquí.

nor here.

Sólo de aquí.

Only from here.

[repetir la rima varias veces]

[repeat the verse several times]

Tortillitas · Corn Tortillas

Corn and flour tortillas are a staple food in many Latin American countries. Tostadas, tacos, nachos, and chips are made from corn tortillas. Burritos, chimichangas, and sopapillas are made from flour tortillas. For this clapping rhyme, the adult holds the child's wrists and helps the child clap while reciting the words. Older children can clap and sing for themselves, alone or in a circle.

Tortillitas de manteca
pa' mamá que está contenta.
Tortillitas de salvado
pa' papá que está enojado.

Corn tortillas, corn tortillas,
corn tortillas for my mommy.
Flour tortillas, flour tortillas,
flour tortillas for my daddy.

[repetir la rima]

[repeat the verse]

Este compró · This One Bought
un huevito   a Little Egg

Starting with the baby finger, touch each finger of one hand as you say the rhyme.

Este compró un huevito.

This one bought a little egg.

Este encendió el fuego.

This one lit the fire.

Este trajo la sal.

This one brought the salt.

Este lo guisó.

This one was the cook.

Y este pícaro gordo ¡se lo comió!

And this chubby, chubby one ate it all up!